TABLE OF CONTENTS

© Copyright 1996, Teaching Ink, Inc.

ABOUT THIS BOOK

This book is designed to help your students become confident problem solvers. Some problems may have more than one correct answer as does real life. There also may be a few ways to solve some problems. The focus of this book is on the processes that are used to find solutions to problems. If students are equipped with knowledge of different processes they can use, they will be able to tackle any problem. Today's jobs require the ability to analyze situations and figure out solutions.

Even though most math is designed with one correct answer in mind, as teachers we should be willing to learn that there may be more than one right answer. According to the NCTM (National Council of Teachers of Mathematics) guidelines, students realize there can be more than one right answer when open-ended problems are posed. Sometimes the answer is not what is important. It is more important that the student has learned how to use deductive reasoning skills and apply different strategies appropriately. It is our hope that this book will help teachers and students sharpen problem solving skills, which will be needed now and in the 21st Century.

RUBRIC FOR EVALUATION OF PROBLEM SOLVING

In this book we have enabled students to become fully aware of the key elements to use in a successful evaluation. We have asked them not only what their answer is, but to explain their answer in words. In this manner teachers can see what students are thinking as well as how well they can derive a solution. There may be many ways to solve some problems and this is encouraged.

Allowing students to write a response in math permits the teacher to understand what principles and processes the student fully understands. Sometimes students will make mechanical errors, but the strategy chosen is correct.

Ideally, the written response should explain the process used and why it was chosen. The computation part of the problem should be judged separately. At the back of the book we have included an "Explanation/Computation" plan sheet for your convenience.

The following Rubric is a guide to follow when evaluating problem solving math problems.

PROBLEM SOLVER YEAH!

Students understand the mathematical concepts and principles involved and apply them appropriately.

Students give a complete written explanation telling what was done and why it was done.

Students are able to show a complete relationship among the components. Computations are accurate and complete. Students show a complete relationship among the components.

If a student uses a diagram it is explained.

PROBLEM SOLVER O.K.!

Students show some basic understanding of math concepts and apply appropriate math strategies for the problem.

Students may have some computational errors.

Students give some explanation of the problem.

Students may say why a process is used but the explanation is not complete.

Students may include a diagram or drawing with some explanation.

PROBLEM SOLVER NAY!

Students show limited or no understanding of the math problem.

Students may have major computational errors.

Students may use an inappropriate strategy.

Students may use irrelevant information.

Students provide minimal explanation of the problem.

The explanation does not match the solution.

There is no written explanation or strategy.

MAKE A PICTURE OR DRAW A DIAGRAM

Sometimes it helps to make a simple drawing to help you see what is happening in a story problem. A drawing may help you understand and work with the information in the problem.

EXAMPLE:

Temika had to go to her mother's friend's house after school. She didn't know how to get there so Kimlee drew her a map. Kimlee replied, "Here we are at the school on the corner of Lincoln Lane and Ridge Road. Go forward 3 blocks on Lincoln Lane. Turn right on Baker Street and go forward 3 blocks. Turn left on Hay Street. Go forward 4 blocks to Timber Lane. Your mother's friend's house is on the corner of Timber Lane and Hay Street." Can you show Kimlee's path to Temika's mother's friend's house? Show your work and explain your answer.

In order to solve the problem you have to first find out what Kimlee is doing for Temika. She is drawing a map and giving her directions to Temika's mother's friend's house. What directions did Kimlee give her? Start at the school on the corner of Lincoln Lane and Ridge Road. Go forward 3 blocks on Lincoln Lane. Turn right on Baker Street and go forward 3 blocks. Turn left on Hay Street. Go forward 4 blocks to Timber Lane. What was at the corner of Timber Lane and Hay Street? Temika's mother's friend's house. If you use graph paper, each square can represent one block. Begin your map at the school on the corner of Lincoln Lane and Ridge Road. Use a pencil to trace the path and write in the street names. How many blocks must Temika go forward on Lincoln Lane? 3 What street will she come to? Baker Street. What direction must she go on Baker Street? Right and go 3 blocks. What street does she come to? Hay Street. What direction must she go on Hay Street? Left and go 4 blocks. What street will she come to? Timber Lane. What is at the corner of Timber Lane and Hay Street? Temika's mother's friend's house.

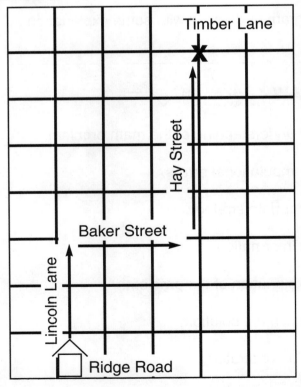

PROBLEM #1

Eight children at the birthday party want to share 24 cupcakes equally. How many cupcakes should each child get? Show your work and explain your answer.

PROBLEM #2

A checkerboard has 25 squares. Some are black and some are white. Squares of the same color are never next to each other. Draw a diagram or picture to answer the question. Explain how you got your answer. HINT: if the square in one corner is black, what color is the square in the opposite corner?

PROBLEM #3

Several football teams are having an "End of the Season" party. The team captains are putting square tables together in a long row for the party. They can put two chairs on each side of the table. The tables are all the same size. If they put 10 tables together in a row, how many people can sit down at the party? Show your work and explain your answer.

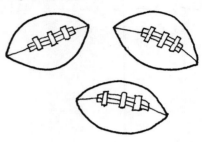

PROBLEM #4

Rich is looking for friends to play soccer. His friends live on his side of the street. First he goes down the hill 4 houses to get Nick. Nick lives in the first house on the block. Then Rich goes up the hill 6 houses to get Herbert. From here he goes up the hill 13 houses to get Malik. He lives in the last house on the block. How many houses are on Rich's side of the street in his block? Show your work and explain your answer.

PROBLEM #5

The scout troop's trip this summer was to explore rivers by canoe. Their first adventure was to go from one end of Carson River to the other. They started out at Deep Creek Harbour and paddled 7 miles south to one end of the river. The next day they paddled 9 miles north to Deadman's Cove. When a storm came up, they turned around and paddled 5 miles south to Silverhook Park. They camped there overnight. The next day they paddled 12 miles north to the other end of the river. How many miles long is Carson River? Show your work and explain your answer.

PROBLEM #6

Marvin the Mailman delivers packages daily to an office building. Today he started on the first floor and went up 7 floors. Then he went down 3 floors, and then up 16 floors. He went up 2 more floors to the top of the building. How many floors were in the office building? Show your work and explain your answer.

MAKE A PICTURE OR DRAW A DIAGRAM ANSWERS

PROBLEM #1

To solve the problem you would divide 24 by 8 to show how many cupcakes each child received at the birthday party, (24 divided by 8 = 3 cupcakes). Your students may want to draw out 24 cupcakes and group them in sets of 8 with three in each group.

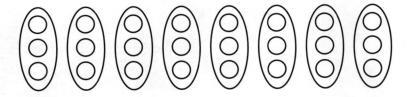

PROBLEM #2

Drawing a diagram or picture of the checkerboard will help the students visualize the problem better. The square in the opposite corner is black.

B	W	B	W	B
W	B	W	B	W
B	W	B	W	B
W	B	W	B	W
B	W	B	W	B

B = Black
W = White

PROBLEM #3

This problem can be solved in a variety of ways depending on how you set up the tables. A diagram will help solve this problem. 44 people can sit at the table if you count four at each table and two on each end.

$$44= \begin{array}{c} \text{xx xx xx xx xx xx xx xx xx xx} \\ {}^{\text{x}}_{\text{x}}\boxed{6}\ \boxed{4}\ \boxed{4}\ \boxed{4}\ \boxed{4}\ \boxed{4}\ \boxed{4}\ \boxed{4}\ \boxed{4}\ \boxed{6}{}^{\text{x}}_{\text{x}} \\ \text{xx xx xx xx xx xx xx xx xx xx} \end{array}$$

or

80 people can sit at the table if you have 10 tables with 8 people at them.

$$80=$$

PROBLEM #4

Drawing a picture or diagram may help you solve this problem. In order to solve the problem you need to figure out how many houses are on Rich's side of the street. According to the diagram, there are 20 houses on Rich's side of the street.

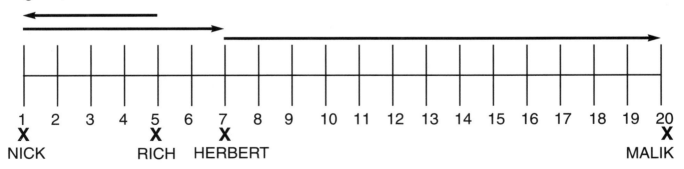

9

PROBLEM #5

A diagram or picture will help you solve this problem. You want to find out how many miles long is Carson River. Start at Deep Creek Harbour and go 7 miles south to one end of the river. Next, they went 9 miles north to Deadman's Cove. After the storm they paddled 5 miles south to Silverhook Park and camped overnight. Then finally they paddled 12 miles north to the opposite end of Carson River. According to the diagram the river is16 miles long.

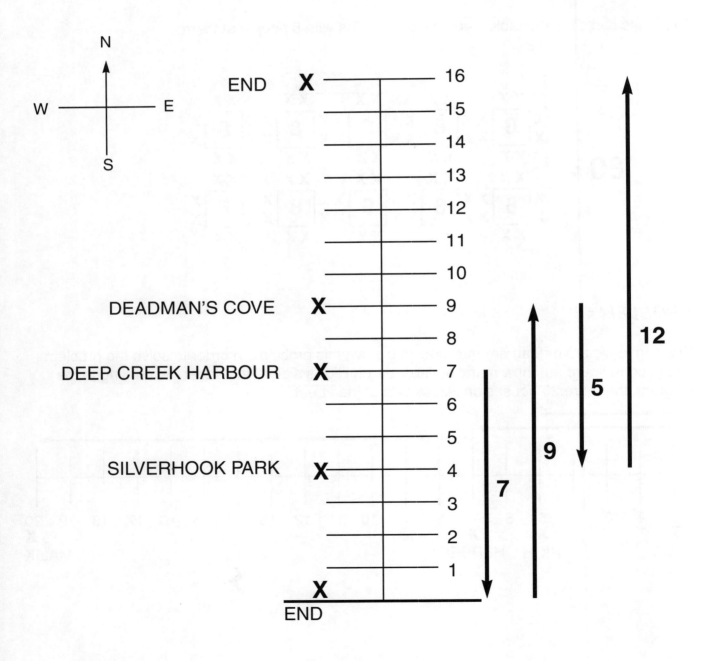

PROBLEM #6

In order to figure out the answer to the problem you need to draw a picture or diagram of the office building.

$$7-3=4 \quad 4+16=20 \quad 20+2=22$$

+2

+16

-3

+7

22 —————

11

MAKE IT SIMPLER

Complicated problems may be less confusing by breaking down the problem to make it easier to solve. This can be done by using smaller numbers, especially less than 10, or by reducing the number of items given in the problem. By using simpler problems, you may want to use an organized list or table to help you solve the problem.

EXAMPLE:

Two people boarded the tour bus at the first stop. Four people boarded at the second stop, six people boarded at the third stop, and so forth. If this pattern continues, how many passengers will be on the bus after the seventh stop.

To simplify the problem make an organized list and look for a pattern. Your list should contain the number of people who board the bus and the number of stops. In order to find how many passengers there are on the bus, total the number of people at each stop.

2+4+6+8+10+12+14=56 passengers on the bus

STOP	PEOPLE
1	2
2	4
3	6
4	8
5	10
6	12
7	14

PROBLEM #1

There are 3 golf balls in each box. How many golf balls are in 5 boxes? Show your work and explain your answer.

PROBLEM #2

A cookie recipe calls for 4 cups of flour for every 3 cups of sugar. How many cups of flour are needed for 18 cups of sugar? Show your work and explain your answer.

13

PROBLEM #3

Gina made a large tunnel of cardboard boxes in the basement. She got 15 boxes. She cut 2 sides off each box and then put the boxes together like this. See sample. Assume that there are 6 sides to a box before it is cut.

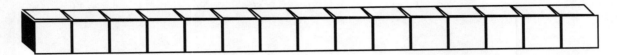

One day they had a terrible flood and it flooded her basement. All the sides of the boxes that were not touching the basement floor got soaked. How many sides got wet? Show your work and explain your answer.

boxes   sides

PROBLEM #4

The mailman's job is to stamps the sides of the packages as they come into his post office. He stamps the sides that are not touching the floor of the mailroom and not touching another box. Today there are 25 packages on the floor in the mailroom. The mailman put the packages in 5 stacks, and the sides of the stacks touch. How many sides of the packages must the mailman stamp? Show your work and explain your answer.

PROBLEM #5

Renee is 10 years old. Her mom is three times as old. How old will Renee be when her mom is twice as old as she is? Show your work and explain your answer.

PROBLEM #6

Robby's Breakfast Buffet offers a choice of 2 juices or milk with either pancakes, crepes, or french toast. How many possible different breakfasts could you have at Robby's Breakfast Buffet? Show your work and explain your answer.

MAKE IT SIMPLER ANSWERS

PROBLEM #1

In order to make this problem simpler, a chart would be helpful for some students.   15 golf balls in 5 boxes.

3 x 5 = 15

NUMBER OF BOXES	1	2	3	4	5
NUMBER OF GOLF BALLS	3	6	9	12	15

PROBLEM #2

In order to figure out this problem and make it simpler, a chart would help some students.
24 cups of flour are needed for 18 cups of sugar.

4 x 6 =24   3 x 6 =18

FLOUR	4	8	12	16	20	24
SUGAR	3	6	9	12	15	18

PROBLEM #3

In order to figure out how many sides got wet in the basement you may need to make a chart. This may make the problem simpler for some students. A diagram may help also. Remember, there are 4 possible sides for each box. 45 sides got wet.

BOXES	SIDES
1	3
2	6
3	9
4	12
5	15
6	18
7	21
8	24
9	27
10	30
11	33
12	36
13	39
14	42
15	45

17

PROBLEM #4

In order to make this problem simpler, a chart would help the students visualize the packages the mailman is stamping.

PACKAGES	5	10	15	20	25
SIDES STAMPED	21	32	43	54	65

PROBLEM #5

In order to make this problem simpler, a chart would help the students visualize the ages of Renee and her mom.

RENEE	10	12	14	16	18	20
MOM	30	32	34	36	38	40

PROBLEM #6

In order to figure out what the breakfast buffet offers, a diagram or drawing may help the students see what is offered.

9 BREAKFAST CHOICES

1   JUICE ———— CREPES
                PANCAKES
                FRENCH TOAST

MILK ———— CREPES
             PANCAKES
             FRENCH TOAST

2   JUICE ———— CREPES
                PANCAKES
                FRENCH TOAST

WORK BACKWARDS

These problems require students to start with data given at the end of the problem, work backwards and end with data presented at the beginning of the problem.

EXAMPLE

Betty was studying elephants. She went to the library and checked out all the books she could find on the subject. Laurie, her friend, took 5 of the books because she was interested in elephants too. Four of her other friends each took a book. When she counted her books, she only had 9 books left. How many books did she check out of the library? Show your work and explain your answer.

ANSWER

We know that Betty had 9 books left. Four of her friends took books, so we will add 4 + 9 = 13. Then we know that Laurie also borrowed 5 books, so we will add these 5 books :
4 + 9 + 5 = 18. Betty had checked out 18 books from the library.

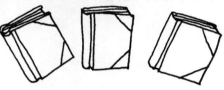

PROBLEM #1

The Johnson family went on a hiking trip in the mountains. They brought lots of licorice with them to eat on the trip. They ate red licorice on Monday. They ate 4 fewer sticks of licorice on Tuesday than on Monday. They ate 4 fewer sticks of licorice on Wednesday and 4 fewer on Thursday. Each day they ate 4 fewer sticks than the day before. On Thursday they finished the last 8 sticks of licorice. How many sticks of licorice did the Johnson family take with them on their hiking trip? Show all of your work and explain.

PROBLEM #2

Brandon had a collection of books. He brought his collection to school to share with the rest of the class. Five children immediately took books home. The second day 6 more children took Brandon's books home to read. The third day 1/2 as many kids borrowed books as had borrowed them on the second day. On the fourth day Brandon realized there were only 18 books left. How many books did Brandon bring to school? Show your work and explain your answer.

21

PROBLEM #3

Jack collected football cards. He brought his collection to school every day because the kids traded cards at recess. Monday he brought all of his cards to school. He brought them home and counted them. On Tuesday, he brought his cards to school. When he got home he found that he was missing 5 cards. Wednesday he brought his cards to school. When he got home he found that he was missing 5 more cards. On Thursday he counted that he had 357 cards. How many cards did he have in his collection on Monday? Show your work and explain your answer.

PROBLEM #4

Doug loves to eat chocolate candies so much that he keeps them in a special dish. He counts how many he has every day. On Monday he counted them and found that 7 candies were missing. On Tuesday he found that 7 more were missing. On Wednesday he found that 7 more were missing. On Thursday he counted that there were only 296 chocolate candies left. How many chocolate candies did he start out with? Show your work and explain your answer.

PROBLEM #5

Peter played basketball everyday after school. He played on Monday and had a great time. On Tuesday he scored 3 fewer points than the day before. On Wednesday he scored 3 fewer points than on Tuesday. Each day he scored 3 fewer points than the day before. On Thursday he scored 31 points in all. How many points did he score on Monday? Show your work and explain your answer.

PROBLEM #6

Cindy brought a lot of carrots to school for her lunch. The lunch time was at 1 o'clock. At 9 a.m. she got hungry and ate 5 of her carrots. At 10 a.m. she ate 5 more carrots. At 11 a.m. she ate 5 more carrots. At 12 o'clock she ate 5 more carrots than at 11 a.m. By 1 o'clock she looked in her lunch bag and was very upset. She only had 3 carrots left! How many carrots did she bring to school in the morning? Show your work and explain your answer.

WORK BACKWARDS ANSWERS

PROBLEM #1

Working backwards, there were 8 sticks of licorice left on Thursday. Wednesday they ate 4 more sticks (8 + 4 = 12). On Tuesday they ate 4 more sticks than on Wednesday (12 + 4 = 16). And on Monday there were 4 more sticks (16 + 4 = 20). They ate 56 sticks of licorice on their trip (8 + 12 + 16 + 20 = 56).

PROBLEM #2

We know that Brandon had 18 books on the fourth day. Working backwards, the third day he had half as many as on the second day (1/2 of 6 = 3). We will also add the five books that were taken as soon as Brandon got to school. Add these numbers together and we will know how many books Brandon brought to school (18 + 3 + 6 + 5 = 32).

PROBLEM #3

We know that Jack had 357 cards on Thursday. Working backwards, add the 5 cards that were lost on Wednesday (357 + 5 = 362). Then add the 5 cards that were lost on Tuesday (357 + 5 + 5 = 367).

Another way to do this problem would be to group all of the cards that were lost (5 + 5 = 10) and then add this to 357.

PROBLEM #4

We know that Doug had 296 chocolate candies on Thursday. We then add the candies that were missing on Wednesday, Tuesday, and Monday (296 + 7 + 7 + 7 = 317).

Another way of doing this problem would be to see that there were 7 chocolate candies missing for 3 days (3x7 = 21) and then add this to 296.

PROBLEM #5

We know that Peter scored 31 points on Thursday. He scored 3 more points on Wednesday (34). He scored 3 more points on Tuesday than on Wednesday (37) and 3 more points on Monday (40).

Another way of doing this would be to multiply 3x3 and then add that to 31.

PROBLEM #6

We know that there are only 3 carrots left at 1 o'clock. Add 5 carrots that were eaten at 12 o'clock (3 + 5 = 8). Then add 5 more carrots that were eaten at 11 a.m. (8 + 5 = 13). Then add 5 carrots that were eaten at 10 a.m. (13 + 5 = 18). And then add the 5 carrots that she ate at 9 a.m. (18 + 5 = 23). She brought 23 carrots to school.

ACT IT OUT OR USE OBJECTS

Sometimes you can see what happens in a problem by acting it out or using objects you can move around. This activity can help you remember the process for use with other problems of the same kind. Simple objects such as cubes, paper scraps, and other various manipulatives can be used to solve these kinds of problems.

EXAMPLE:

Marc keeps his video games on a shelf in the family room. Rocky Ranger is in front of Bandits. His Bandits game is on the left side of Rocky Ranger. Knights and Dragons is between Bandits and Dinosaur Fun. Dinosaur Fun is behind the Lots of Magic game. Where is each game on Marc's shelf?

You could very easily act out this problem by assigning a student to each video game and having them move according to what the problem tells you to do.

You may also use objects such as paper, chips or even better yet, old videos with the problem names on them. In order to solve the problem, you have to decide where you will put each video. A chart may help you understand the problem better.

Dinosaur Fun	Knights and Dragons	Bandits
Lots of Magic	Robbers	Rocky Ranger

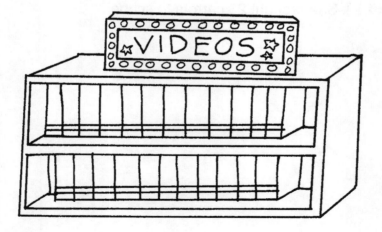

PROBLEM #1

Three cheerleaders stood in a row on the floor of the gym. Three more cheerleaders climbed up onto the shoulders of the first three cheerleaders. Melissa climbed onto T.J.'s shoulders. Steve stood next to Melissa, and Alison stood between T.J. and Phil. Jill climbed onto Phil's shoulders. What is the name of each cheerleader shown below? Show your work and explain your answer.

PROBLEM #2

There's a parking garage at the mall. Six cars are parked in the lot. The red car is parked in front of the green car. A white car is parked between the green car and a purple car. A green car is parked on the right side of the red car, and an orange car is parked in front of the purple car. What color is each car shown in the parking lot below? Show your work and explain your answer.

27

PROBLEM #3

Joe was the fifth person in line at the movies. John was three places in front of Joe. Nine places behind John is Jana. What place in line is Jana? Show your work and explain your answer. Sometimes if you "act out" the problem, you can solve it more easily.

PROBLEM #4

Katie had 5 pennies, 3 nickels, 6 dimes, and 4 quarters with which to make change. She gave out $1.16 in change using only 7 coins. How many of each coin did she have left? Show your work and explain your answer.

PROBLEM #5

Mr. Burke, the gym teacher is redecorating the gym into very colorful colors for the next game. He is painting one wall with squares of white, pink, blue, and orange. He divided the wall into 4 columns with 4 rows. Before painting he marked each square with W, P, B, or O. He didn't want any color repeated in the same row or in the same column. How did Mr. Burke arrange the colors in the squares on the gym wall? Show your work and explain your answer.

PROBLEM #6

The Student Council set up a display for the school store. The display case had 5 columns and 5 rows. They put 5 pencils, 5 notebooks, 5 erasers, 5 glues, and 5 folders in the case for display. The Student Council President told the workers to be sure to have 5 different things in each column and each row. How did they set up the display for the school store? Show your work and explain your answer.

29

ACT IT OUT OR USE OBJECTS ANSWERS

PROBLEM #1

In order to answer the problem you may need to make a chart of the cheerleaders. You can answer this problem several ways. You also may want your students to act out this problem, it might make it easier.

MELISSA	STEVE	JILL
T.J.	ALISON	PHIL

OR

JILL	STEVE	MELISSA
PHIL	ALISON	T.J.

PROBLEM #2

In order to solve this problem you may need colored pieces of paper or chips to help figure out the answer. You want to find out what color each car is in the mall parking lot. A chart may make the problem simpler.

RED	GREEN	ORANGE
GREEN	WHITE	PURPLE

PROBLEM #3

Sometimes if you act out the problem you can solve the problem more easily. To find what place Jana is in line, have several students form a line. You will need about 15 students for your acting out part. Joe was the 5th person in line. John was 3 places in front of Joe. John was #2 in line and Jana was 9 places in back of Joe. Jana is in the 11th place.

30

PROBLEM #4

In order to solve this problem you may want to use real coins or play money. Katie had 0 quarters, 5 dimes, 2 nickels, and 4 pennies left.

PROBLEM #5

In order to figure out the problem a chart will help you see the pattern Mr. Burke was trying to make on the gym wall. Colored pieces of paper will also help you see the pattern.

WHITE	PINK	BLUE	ORANGE
ORANGE	BLUE	PINK	WHITE
PINK	WHITE	ORANGE	BLUE
BLUE	ORANGE	WHITE	PINK

PROBLEM #6

To solve this problem you may need to use markers or manipulative the squares to make it easier. A chart also will help you solve the problem.

pencil = P   notebook = N   eraser = E   glue = G   folder = F

P	N	E	F	G
G	E	P	N	F
N	G	F	E	P
F	P	N	G	E
E	F	G	P	N

LOOK FOR A PATTERN

A pattern is something that repeats itself over and over. Looking for patterns is an important strategy to use in problem solving. Sometimes a problem can be solved just by recognizing the pattern or by extending a pattern to find the solution. A number table will often reveal patterns, and is frequently used with this strategy.

EXAMPLE

On Monday, Janet had to practice the piano. The first time she practiced, she played for 10 minutes. The second time she practiced, she played for 20 minutes. On Wednesday, she practiced for 30 minutes. She was having such a great time that the 4th time she practiced she played for 40 minutes. On what day would she be practicing for 1 1/2 hours? Show your work and explain your answer.

ANSWER:

Look to see if there is a number pattern that is the same throughout the problem. Then set up a table to project what the times will be.

Students will need to know that 1 hour equals 60 minutes. 1 1/2 hours equals 90 minutes. On Tuesday, the 9th day, she will be practicing for 1 1/2 hours.

Times:	1	2	3	4	5	6	7	8	9
Minutes:	10	20	30	40	50	60	70	80	90
Days:	M	Tu	W	Th	F	S	S	M	Tu

33

PROBLEM #1

Sam joined a video club that sent him videos every month. In January he received 2 videos. The second month he got 5 videos in the mail. In March he received 7 videos. And in April he received 10 videos. How many videos will Sam receive in July? Show your work and explain your answer.

PROBLEM #2

Randy's baby sister was a very tiny baby when she was born. She only weighed 4 pounds 6 ounces. When she went for her first month check-up she had gained 6 ounces. When she went for her 2nd month check-up she had gained 12 ounces. When she went for her 3 month check-up she had gained 18 ounces (or 1 pound 2 ounces). How much will she weigh at her 6 month check-up if she continues to grow in the same manner? Remember: 1 pound equals 16 ounces. Show your work and explain your answer.

34

PROBLEM #3

Jodie had a special ring. Every time she wore it something special happened. The first time she wore it, she found a quarter. The second time she wore it she found a dollar. The third time she wore it she found a dollar and three quarters ($1.75). If she keeps on being so lucky when she wears it, how many more times will she have to wear it to find $4? Show your work and explain your answer.

PROBLEM #4

Jeff found an old chest in the attic. It was filled with boxes. In the first box he found 11 cents. In the second box he found 16 cents. In the third box he found 21 cents. There was a total of 6 boxes in the old chest. How much money did he find in the attic?

PROBLEM #5

Fred has a mystery jacket. Every time he puts it on, he finds marbles in his pocket. Monday he found 3 marbles in his pocket. Tuesday he found 7 marbles in his jacket pocket. Wednesday he found 11 marbles in his pocket. How many marbles will he find if he wears the jacket 4 more times?

PROBLEM #6

Katie was in a walk-a-thon. She had gotten pledges that totaled four dollars for every mile that she walked. In the first hour she walked 3 miles. In the second hour she walked 3 more miles. And in the third hour she walked 3 more miles. If she continued in the walk-a-thon for four more hours, how much money would Katie have collected?

36

LOOK FOR A PATTERN ANSWERS

PROBLEM #1

In order to see how many videos Sam will receive in July we will need to see if there is some kind of pattern in the number of videos he is receiving. Once we have figured out this pattern, we will need to continue the pattern so that we can project the number of videos Sam will get in July.

Months	J	F	M	A	M	J	J
Videos	2	5	7	10	12	15	17

The pattern is +3 and then +2.

PROBLEM #2

We need to see if there is some kind of pattern as to how much the baby is gaining. She is gaining 6 more ounces per month. Then we need to project what she will weigh in 6 months.

Months	1	2	3	4	5	6
Weight Gain	6 oz.	12 oz.	18 oz.	24 oz.	30 oz.	36 oz

At 6 months the baby will weigh 36 oz. more than she did at birth. She weighed 4 pounds 6 ounces at birth. Students will need to know that 1 pound equals 16 ounces. Therefore, 36 ounces will equal 2 pounds 4 ounces. This added to the birthweight will tell us what the baby should weigh at 6 months: 6 pounds 10 ounces. This is quite a tiny baby!

This could also be interpreted to say that the baby gained at the first month 6 more ounces than its birthweight (4 lbs. 12 oz.). The second month he/she could have gained 12 ounces more than what it weighed the first month. The third month he/she would have gained 18 oz. more than he/she had gained the second month etc. If this were true, the baby could weigh 4 lbs. 12 oz. at 1 month; 5 lbs. 8 oz. at 2 months; 6 lbs. 10 oz. at three months; 8 lbs. 2 oz. at 4 months; 10 lbs. at 5 month; and 12 lbs. 4 oz. at 6 months.

PROBLEM #3

Students will need to discover what the pattern is. They can subtract 25 cents from $1 to find that it is 75 cents. They will then need to keep adding 75 cents until the amount reaches $4. Students can also draw a pattern to simplify this process.

Number of times worn	1	2	3	4	5	6
Money found	.25¢	$1.00	$1.75	$2.50	$3.25	$4.00

Jodie will have to wear the ring 3 more times.

PROBLEM #4

We need to see if there is some kind of pattern in the amounts of money found. In each box, Jeff finds 5¢ more than the amount in the previous box. We then need to list the amounts and add them up to see how much Jeff found all together.

Boxes	1	2	3	4	5	6
Amount of Money	11¢	16¢	21¢	26¢	31¢	36¢

Jeff found $1.41.

38

PROBLEM #5

We need to project how many marbles Fred will find in his pocket. First, we need to see if there is a number pattern. List the number of marbles that he has found: 3, 7, and 11. Each number in the sequence is 4 more than the previous number. Therefore, continue this number pattern 4 more times. 3, 7, 11, 15, 19, 23, 27. If Fred wears his jacket 4 more times he should find 27 marbles in the pocket.

Number of times worn	1	2	3	4	5	6	7
Marbles	3	7	11	15	19	23	27

PROBLEM #6

We need to see if there is a pattern. It seems that she is walking 3 miles per hour. Therefore, we can project that she will earn $12 per hour.

Miles	3	6	9	12	15	18	21
Money	$12	$24	$36	$48	$64	$80	$84

You could also multiply $4 x 21 = $84

You could also multiply $12 x 7 = $ 84 since you know that Katie walked for 7 hours.

39

MAKING A TABLE

A table is an orderly way of arranging data, such as numbers. It helps keep track of data, spot missing data and identify information that may be asked for in the problem. This strategy is often used in conjunction with other strategies.

EXAMPLE

Thomas brought a birthday treat to school for his classmates. He did not want his friends to know how many lollipops he had brought, so he told them:

> There were more than 35.
> There were less than 50.
> He said the number when he counted by fives.
> He didn't say the number when he counted by 10's.

How many lollipops did Thomas bring to school? Show your work and explain your answer.

ANSWER

The problem states that "there were more than 35". Therefore, 35 will be our first number in our number table. Since the number is less than 50, we will only go as high as 50. We will then list the numbers between 35 and 50 by fives. We will then eliminate those numbers that are multiples of 10.

35   40   45   50

45 is the only number left.

PROBLEM #1

Debby rides a public bus to school. She rides past more than 19 streets. She rides past fewer than 28 streets. She rides past odd numbers only. One part of the number tells how many letters there are in Debby's name. What is the number of streets Debby passes on her way to school? Show your work and explain your answer.

PROBLEM #2

The guard at a theme park compared the number of people who went on two different rides. One guard checked in the people at Ride A. Another guard checked in people at Ride B. What time of day did both guards have the same number of visitors? Show your work and explain your answer.

Time	10:00	11:00	12:00	1:00	2:00	3:00
Ride A	23	67	42	39	68	57
Ride B	21	67	42	39	68	53

41

PROBLEM #3

Michael and Billy are collecting video game cartridges. On Monday they each had 4. On Tuesday Michael had 7 and Billy had 6. On Wednesday Michael had 10 and Billy had 8. On Thursday Michael had 13 and Billy had 10. If they keep getting cartridges in the same way, how many cartridges will Michael have when Billy has 16? Show your work and explain your answer.

PROBLEM #4

Joanne was selling Girl Scout cookies for her troop. She could sell 3 different kinds of cookies. She could sell mint cookies, lemon cookies, and chocolate cookies. For every 5 boxes of mint cookies, she had to sell 3 boxes of lemon cookies, and 2 boxes of chocolate cookies to win a bike.

Joanne sold 40 boxes of different cookies. How many boxes of different cookies did she sell? Show your work and explain your answer.

42

PROBLEM #5

David was complaining that he had so much homework. He had spelling homework every second night. He had social studies homework every fourth night. And he had math homework every eighth night. How many times during the 1st week did he have homework in two subjects? What night in the first week did he not have any homework? Show your work and explain your answer.

PROBLEM #6

Gene loved to count different kinds of cars when he travelled with his family. He saw 12 Chevrolets, 5 Pontiacs, 13 Cadillacs, and 5 Mazdas. If Gene counted 10 Mazdas, how many cars in all did he count? How many of each kind did he see? Show your work and explain your answer.

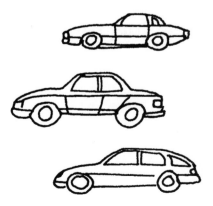

43

PROBLEM #1

The clues tell us that the number table should start at 19 and go until 28. We should list odd numbers only. Then we need to count the letters in her name.

19   21   23   (25)   27   28

PROBLEM #2

Students should be able to read the table and understand that the times go across in a line. Students will also have to read the table up and down. The rides are listed underneath the times and the number of people who went on the rides are listed under the appropriate times. Reading across you will see that both rides had the same number of people at 11:00, 12:00, 1:00, and 2:00.

PROBLEM #3

You need to set up a table so that you can see the number pattern. Michael's numbers increase by 3 and Billy's numbers increase by 2. When Billy has 16 cartridges Michael will have 22 cartridges.

	M	Tu	W	Th	F	S	S
Michael	4	7	10	13	16	19	22
Billy	4	6	8	10	12	14	16

PROBLEM #4

In order to find out the proportions of mint to lemon to chocolate, you need to make a table. For each set of 5 mints sold...

MINT	LEMON	CHOCOLATE	TOTAL
5	3	2	**10**
10	6	4	**20**
15	9	6	**30**
20	12	8	**40**

PROBLEM #5

You need to make a table for a week Monday -Friday.

	M	T	W	TH	F
SPELLING		x		x	
SOC. STUDIES				x	

Thursday David would have homework in two subjects. He wouldn't have any homework on Monday, Wednesday, or Friday.

PROBLEM #6

In order to find out how many different kinds of cars that Gene saw, we need to organize the information. Making a table simplifies the information so that we can see what information we have and what we need. Therefore, list the kinds of cars and the numbers that he counted. Since he originally counted 5 Mazdas and later on counted 10 Mazdas, we need to find what relationship these two numbers have. 10 is 2 x 5. Thus, if we multiply all of the other types of cars by 2 we should have the answers. He saw 24 Chevrolets, 10 Pontiacs, and 26 Cadillacs.

Another possible solution would be to say that the relationship between 5 and 10 is that it is 5 more than 10. Therefore you could add 5 more to all of the other car numbers. In that case he would have seen 18 Cadillacs, 10 Pontiacs, and 17 Chevrolets.

		x2	+5
CHEVROLETS	12	24	17
PONTIACS	5	10	10
CADILLACS	13	26	18
MAZDAS	5	10	10

46

GUESS AND CHECK

Guessing and checking is used when a problem has large numbers and many pieces of data, or when one solution is called for and not all possible answers are needed. Students should make a guess and then test to see if they are correct. Sometimes a few guesses have to be made.

EXAMPLE

Tina and Tanya were twin girls who shared everything. They wanted to buy a pair of jeans together that they could share. Together they paid $25. Tina paid $5 more than Tanya. How much did each girl pay?

ANSWER

If Tina paid $15, Tanya paid $15 - $5 = $10.
$10 + $15 = $25.

PROBLEM #1

Karen has a beautiful jewelry collection of 34 different pieces. She has 6 fewer necklaces than bracelets. How many bracelets does she have? How many necklaces does she have? Show your work and explain your answer.

PROBLEM #2

Jeff and Peter bought a package of gum together for 40 cents. Jeff paid 10 cents less than Peter. How much money did each of the boys pay? Show your work and explain your answer.

GUM

48

PROBLEM #3

There was a Boy Scout meeting with the boys and their parents. Altogether there were 52 people who attended the meeting. There were 22 more parents than children. How many children and how many parents were there? Show your work and explain.

PROBLEM #4

Cindy and Dena bought a game of board game together. The game cost $12. Cindy paid $6 less than Dena. How much money did Cindy pay and how much did Dena pay? Show your work and explain.

PROBLEM #5

Jimmy and Mark were in a swim meet. Jimmy tired out but Mark was able to swim 10 more laps. Together they swam 52 laps. How many laps did each boy swim?

PROBLEM #6

Jody and Judy went to the library to check out books on kangaroos. They found 45 books on kangaroos in the library. Judy had a smaller backpack than Jody, so she checked out 15 fewer books than Jody. How many books did each girl check out?

PROBLEM #1

If Karen had 20 bracelets in her collection, she had 20 - 6 = 14 necklaces. To see if this is correct, 14 + 20 = 34 pieces of jewelry.

PROBLEM #2

We know that the package of gum costs 40 cents. And we know that Jeff paid 10 cents less than Peter. Let's guess that Peter paid 25 cents. To check if this is right, we have to see what Jeff would have paid. Jeff would have paid 10 cents less than 25 cents or 15 cents. Thus, 15 cents + 25 cents = 40 cents.

PROBLEM #3

We know that there were 52 people who attended the meeting. We also know that there were 22 more parents than children. If there were 15 children, there would have been 15 + 22 = 37 parents. 15 children + 37 parents equals 52 people who attended the meeting.

PROBLEM #4

We know that the game cost $12. We also know that Cindy paid $6 less than Dena. If Dena paid $9 then Cindy would have paid $9 - $6 =$3. $9 + $3 = $12.

PROBLEM #5

We know that together the boys swam 52 laps. We also know that Mark swam 10 more laps than Jimmy. If Jimmy swam 21 laps then Mark swam 21 laps + 10 laps or 31 laps. 21 + 31 = 52 laps.

PROBLEM #6

We know that they checked out 45 books together. If Jody checked out 30 books then Judy checked out 15 fewer books (15). 30 + 15 = 45 books.

52

LOGICAL REASONING

Logical reasoning is used in all problem solving. Too much information may be given and students need to evaluate what is important and what is not. Sometimes different possibilities must be eliminated and decisions need to be made. There may be problem conditional statements such as, "IF...THEN...," or "IF...THEN...ELSE...," and students need to recognize these.

EXAMPLE:

Barbara's mom said she could have a birthday party but she could only spend $25.00. The cake cost $12.95. The paper goods cost $6.50. How much money could Barbara spend on prizes for her 8 guests? Show all your work and explain in words how you found your answer. Was there any information you did not need to know?

In order to find out how much money Barbara's mom said she would have left, you would first add $12.95 and $6.50.

$$\begin{array}{r} \$12.95 \\ +\ 6.50 \\ \hline \$19.45 \end{array}$$

You would then subtract this sum from the original $25.00

$$\begin{array}{r} \$25.00 \\ -\ 19.45 \\ \hline \end{array}$$

$5.55 is the amount Barbara can spend on prizes

53

PROBLEM # 1

Three girls can mow 3 lawns in 3 hours. How many lawns can six girls mow in 6 hours? Show your work and explain your answer.

PROBLEM # 2

Jeff was having a birthday party. His mom said he could invite 20 friends. How many packages of plates did Jeff's mom need to buy if 8 plates come in a package. Show all your work and explain your answer.

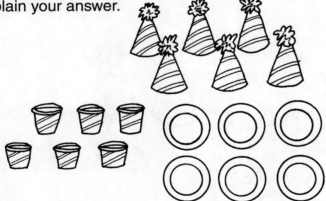

PROBLEM #3

When the Rockets and the Jets play football, they can score only by getting touchdowns and kicking extra points. Bubba Smith is the extra points kicker for the Rockets team. He never misses, so each time they get a touchdown, the Rockets get 7 points. Today they scored 42 points. How many touchdowns did they get? Show your work and explain your answer.

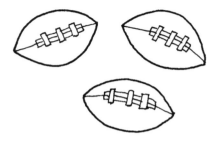

PROBLEM # 4

The Pet Motel is caring for 5 new cats : Fluffy, Buttons, Daisy, Melly, and Pudgy. They put each cat's name on its kennel so they would not get mixed up. What name belongs on each kennel? Show your work and explain your answer.

•Buttons and Melly are calico.
•Melly does not have long ears.
•Daisy is wearing a cat collar.
•Pudgy is so fat and fluffy that he can barely move.

55

PROBLEM #5

Jill and Nikki are on the same team in a Trivia game at school. Each team answers questions that are on blue cards worth 7 points, and yellow cards worth 9 points. Jill and Nikki's team have 128 points and 16 cards so far. How many of the questions were on blue cards and how many were on yellow cards? Show your work and explain your answer.

PROBLEM #6

The baseball uniforms cost $28.75 each. How much would 9 uniforms cost?
Show your work and explain your answer.

LOGICAL REASONING ANSWERS

PROBLEM #1

In order to solve the problem we can figure that three girls can mow three lawns in three hours, and one girl can mow one lawn in three hours. Therefore, six girls can mow 12 lawns in six hours.

OR

If one girl can mow one lawn in 3 hours, then one girl can mow 2 lawns in 6 hours. At the same rate of work per girl, in the same amount of time, 6 girls can mow 12 lawns.
(6 girls x 2 lawns = 12 lawns)

PROBLEM #2

You have to figure 8 plates in a package, so you have to buy three packages in order to have enough for his 20 party guests. Divide 20 by 8 = 2.5 or 2 1/2 packages, you can't buy a half of package, so you buy 3 packages.

PROBLEM #3

In order to figure out the problem of how many touchdowns the Rockets get you have to divide 42 by 7 = 6 touchdowns.

PROBLEM #4

In solving this problem you must think in the logical reasoning strategy of "IF ..THEN" kinds of questions. If you know one thing is true, then you can figure out the rest of the problem. Look for the first clue, Buttons and Melly are calico, can you label them? No. You don't know which cat is Buttons and which cat is Melly. Look at the second clue. Melly does not have long ears. Of the calico cats, which has short ears? Melly. Then the other calico cat is Buttons. Look at the third clue. Daisy is wearing a cat collar. Look at the fourth clue Pudgy's too fat and fluffy to move. Then the last one left is Fluffy.

PROBLEM #5

In order to solve the problem you have to find out how many questions were written on blue cards and how many questions were written on yellow cards. You already know that blue cards are worth 7 points and yellow cards are worth 9 points. Then multiply 7 x 8 = 56 blue cards and 9 x 8 = 72 yellow cards.

PROBLEM #6

To solve this problem multiply $28.75 by 9 = $258.75 for the nine uniforms. You could also add $28.75 nine times to figure out the same answer.

58

EXTRA ACTIVITIES

PROBLEM #1

Laura and Jessica want to ride the new Whamo roller coaster at the local fair. The girls can go into the fair through three different gates. They must stop at the ticket booth that is just inside the gates, and they can take four different routes from the ticket booth to the Whamo roller coaster. How many different paths can Laura and Jessica take from outside the fair to the roller coaster? Show your work and explain your answer.

PROBLEM #2

Mrs. Jones rode the commuter train 4 miles to work, 2 miles to the mall, and 6 miles to her home. It costs $1.50 to ride the train. How many miles did she ride on the commuter train. Show your work and explain your answer.

PROBLEM #3

David had saved his allowance for 6 months. He told his friends that he had saved more than 55 dollars but less than 70 dollars. He said the number when he counted by 5's. He didn't say the number when he counted by 10's. What was the amount of money that he saved? Did he have enough money to buy a bike for 60 dollars? Show your work and explain your answer.

PROBLEM #4

Michelle was learning how to ice skate. She knew that to be a good skater it required a lot of practice. The first day she practiced for 15 minutes. The second day she practiced for 20 minutes. The third day she practiced for 25 minutes. What day will she be practicing for one hour and 10 minutes? Remember, there are 60 minutes in an hour.

PROBLEM #1

In order to solve the problem you may need to make a picture or draw a diagram. You want to figure out how many different routes Laura and Jessica can take from outside the fair to the roller coaster.

3 gates x 4 different routes = 12 possible routes

PROBLEM #2

In order to figure out this problem, you have to choose facts needed to solve the problem. Sometimes a problem has more facts than you need to solve the problem. Find the number of miles Mrs. Jones rode on the commuter train. You know how many miles she rode each time. Find the total of 4 miles, 2 miles, and 6 miles. (You really don't need to know the cost of the train.) Mrs. Jones rode on the commuter train for 12 miles.

$$4 + 2 + 6 = 12$$

4 miles to work
2 miles to the mall
6 miles to her home

PROBLEM #3

The problem states that David saved more than 55 dollars. Therefore, 55 will be our first number in our number table. Since the number has to be less than 70, we will only go as high as 70. We will then list the numbers between 55 and 70 by fives. We will then eliminate those numbers that are multiples of 10.

55   60   65   70

65 is the only number left.

David did have enough money to buy a bike for sixty dollars.

PROBLEM #4

Look to see if there is a number pattern that is consistent throughout the problem. Then set up a table to project what the days will be. She is increasing her practice time by 5 minutes per day.

DAY	1	2	3	4	5	6	7	8	9	10	11	12
MINUTES	15	20	25	30	35	40	45	50	55	60	65	70

Michelle will be practicing for one hour and 10 minutes on the 12th day.

EXPLANATION

COMPUTATION